BIBLE NUMBERS

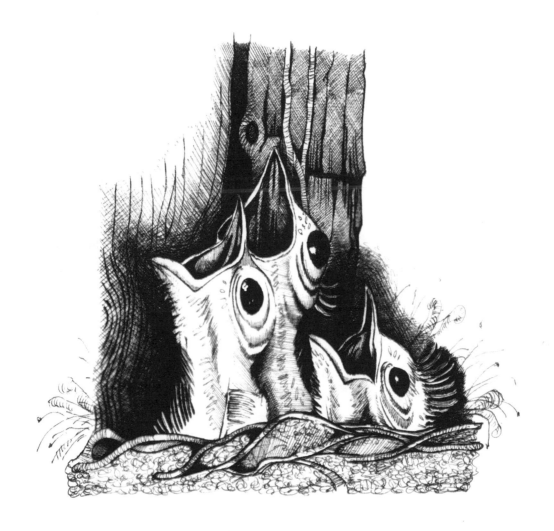

Introducing little children to
simple Bible truths

D1297823

THE BANNER OF TRUTH TRUST
3 Murrayfield Road, Edinburgh EH12 6EL, UK
P.O. Box 621, Carlisle, PA 17013, USA

*

© Alison Brown 2010

ISBN: 978 1 84871 070 2

*

Typeset in Myriad Pro 24/28.8 pt at
The Banner of Truth Trust,
Edinburgh

Graphics TwoFortyFour, Inc.
Wheaton, IL, USA
March 2010
Fr 54187
Printed in Canada

*

Dedicated to my son James,
who also loves
art and teaching.

Colour and Think!

As you colour each number on this page try to think of all the Bible stories you know. Which Bible story does each number remind you of? Here are just some of them....

One Forbidden Tree

Adam and Eve lived in a beautiful garden called Eden. God said they could eat the fruit of every tree but one. The forbidden tree was called The Tree of the Knowledge of Good and Evil. Who persuaded Eve to taste its fruit? (Genesis 3:1-19)

1 = one

Now colour just one of the trees below.

Two Stone Tablets

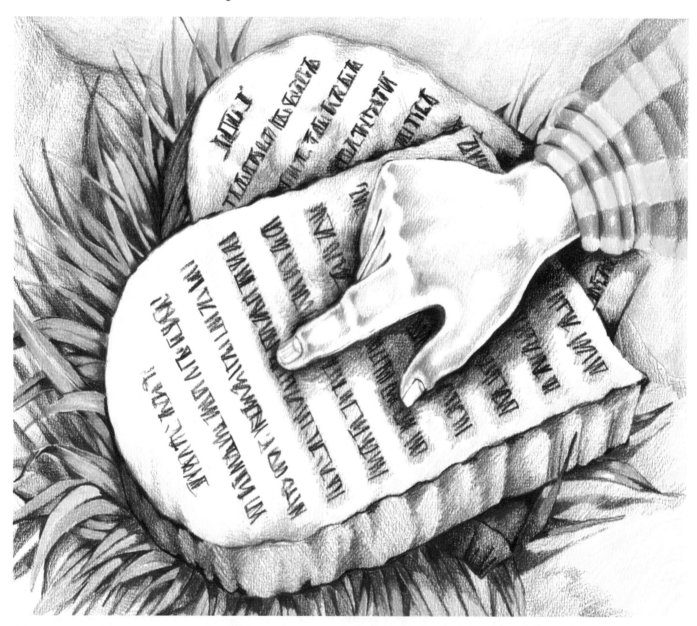

God told Moses to climb to the top of Mount Sinai. Moses stayed there for forty days and forty nights. Then God wrote something very important on two big tablets of stone and gave them to him. What did God write? (Exodus 20:1-17)

2 = two

Now colour just two of the stone tablets below.

Three Special Gifts

When Jesus was a baby he was visited by wise men, who came from a country far away in the east. They brought him three special gifts. First they gave him gold and then they gave him frankincense. What was the third gift? (Matthew 2:1-12)

3 = three

Now colour just three of the gifts below.

9

Four Helpful Friends

In Luke 5:17-24 we read of a man who was very ill and could not walk. Four of his friends carried him, on his bed, up unto a flat roof. They made a big hole in the roof and lowered the man right down into the room below. Why did they do such a strange thing?

4 = four

Now colour just four of the friends below.

Five Smooth Stones

When David the shepherd boy fought Goliath the giant he chose five smooth stones from a little stream. Goliath had a spear and armour but David used only a sling. How many stones were left in his bag when the battle was over? (1 Samuel 17:1-51)

5 = five

Now colour just five of the stones below.

Six Big Waterpots

Jesus was invited to a wedding at Cana. There were many guests at the banquet but there was nothing left to drink. Jesus told the servants to fill six huge waterpots with water. Why was everyone amazed when they poured it out? (John 2:1-11)

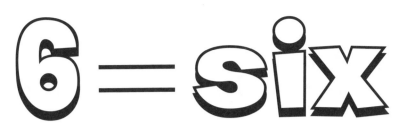

6 = six

Now colour just six of the waterpots below.

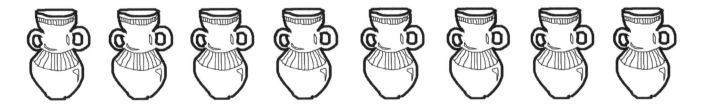

Seven Thin Cows

Pharaoh, the king of Egypt, had a bad dream. It was about seven thin cows eating up seven fat cows! God said the fat cows were a picture of seven years of good harvests and much food. But what did the thin cows in the dream mean? (Genesis 41:15-31)

7 = seven

Now colour just seven of the cows below.

Eight Safe People

We can read about Noah and the ark in Genesis chapters 6 and 7. Noah warned many people about the coming flood but few of them listened. Only eight people believed what God had said. Noah and his wife were two but who were the other six?

8 = eight

Now colour just eight of the people below.

19

Nine Silver Coins

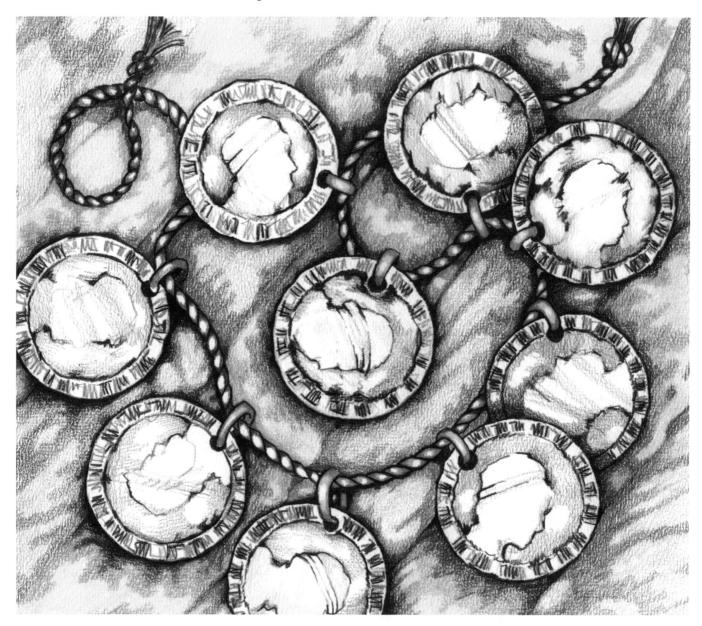

Jesus spoke of a lady who was sad because she had only nine silver coins. She should have had ten but she had lost one. She lit a candle and searched in every dusty corner of her house until she found it! Who helped her celebrate? (Luke 15:8-10)

9 = nine

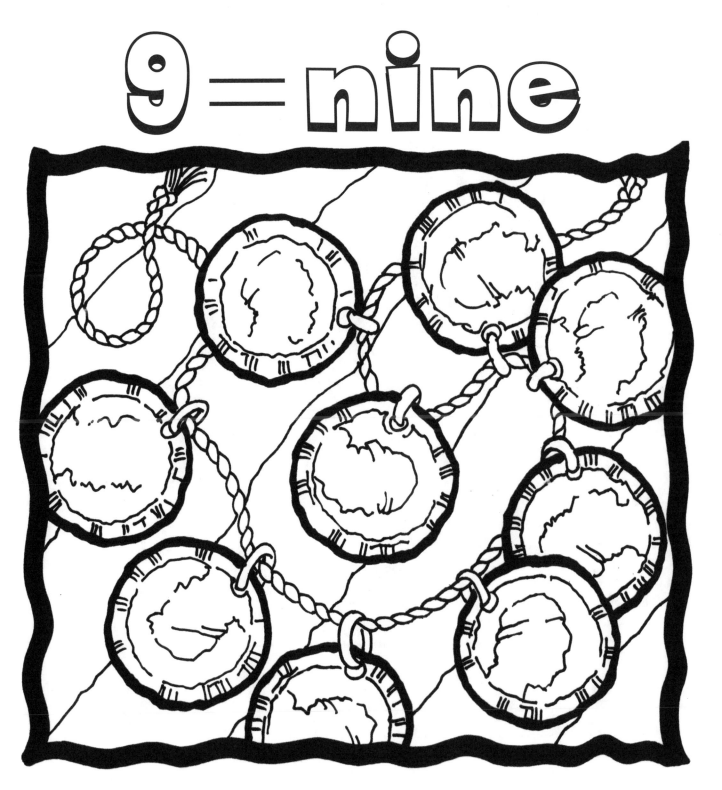

Now colour just nine of the coins below.

Ten Oil Lamps

Ten girls were going to a wedding at night. Five of them brought extra oil for their lamps. The other five brought none, so when their lamps went out, they had to go and buy more, and missed the wedding! Which girls were wise? (Matthew 25:1-13)

10 = ten

Now colour just ten of the oil lamps below.

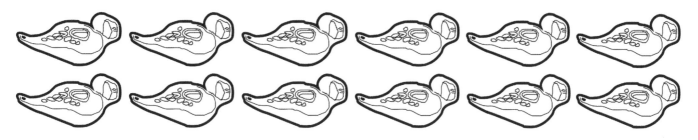

Eleven Full Sacks

These eleven sacks belong to the eleven brothers of Joseph, who was ruler of all Egypt. Some of the brothers went to Egypt several times to bring home something which their families needed very much. What were they bringing home? (Genesis 41:54-57)

11 = eleven

Now colour just eleven of the sacks below.

Twelve Chosen Men

The Bible tells of twelve men who were very close friends of Jesus. Their names were Peter, Andrew, James, John, Philip, Nathanael, Thomas, Matthew, James, Thaddaeus, Simon and Judas. Which four were fishermen? (Matthew 4:18-22)

12 = twelve

Now colour just twelve of the men below.

How Many?

Can you join each picture to the correct number?

12   7

    4

5   9

    6

1   2

    10

3   11

    8

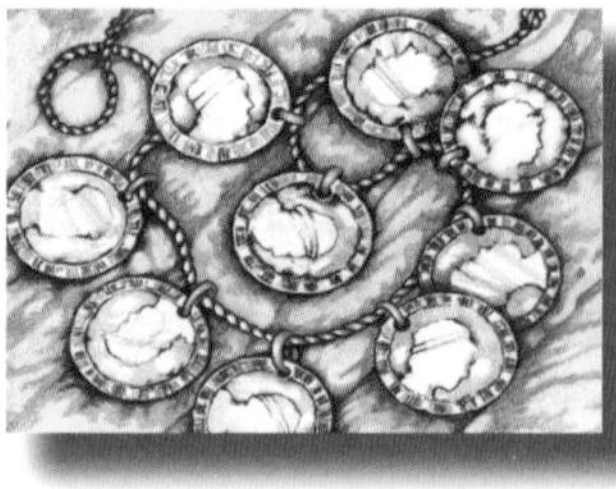

Now, *you* can draw the same twelve pictures in a different order, to tell a wonderful story!

Draw One Forbidden Tree
God's perfect creation changed completely when Adam and Eve sinned. Sin spoiled the world and made a great big gap between people and God.
(Romans 3:23)

Draw Two Stone Tablets
We learn much about God when we read his commandments. God is completely holy and he hates sin, even the smallest unclean thought.
(Psalm 99:9)

Draw Five Smooth Stones
God can do anything. Nothing is too big or too difficult for him. He often uses little things and ordinary people to show us just how mighty he is!
(Luke 1:37)

Draw Seven Thin Cattle

God knows all about everything. He knows exactly what is going to happen and when. God does not have to wonder or guess. (Psalm 147:5)

Draw Three Special Gifts

God knew we needed a Redeemer. He sent his own Son Jesus down to earth to pay for our forgiveness. Jesus died to bridge the gap caused by sin. (John 3:16)

Draw Six Big Waterpots

Jesus has power over all of nature. He rode an untamed donkey and sent fish into a net. He calmed the wind and stilled a stormy sea! (Matthew 28:18)

Draw Four Helpful Friends

Jesus healed many sick people who were lame or had diseases. He brought some who had died back to life. He is the giver of life. (John 10:10b)

Draw Nine Silver Coins

Jesus' love is very great. Though we are far away from God he will keep on searching until he finds the one who is lost or missing. (Luke 19:10)

Draw Ten Oil Lamps

The oil lamps teach us about preparation. We need to prepare for a great celebration in heaven. If we do not we will miss it! (Mark 1:15)

1 2 3 4 5 6 7 8 9 10 11 12

Draw Eight Safe People

If we ask Jesus to forgive our sins and be our Saviour he will prepare us for heaven. He will be our ark and keep us safe through all eternity! (Romans 10:13)

Draw Twelve Chosen Men

The disciples understood who Jesus was. They knew he had come from heaven to be the Redeemer. They wanted the whole world to know. (1 Timothy 1:15)

Draw Eleven Full Sacks

God has promised to take care of everyone who trusts in Jesus and becomes a child of God. He will provide for his children. (Philippians 4:19)